by Ronnie Walter

Volume Two

The Coloring Cafe-Volume Two/Ronnie Walter
ISBN:978-0-98982665-5

Welcome to The Coloring Café™!

Hello!

Inside are 48 pages for you to color, all hand illustrated for your enjoyment. It's well known that the act of coloring calms your mind and relaxes your body with its gentle repetitive motion and creative release--but it's also fun!

I recommend using fine tipped markers, colored pencils, watercolor pencils or pan watercolors. All can be found at any local craft store or online. A heavy application of paint can make the paper buckle a bit so I would use a light hand when using water based paints. Some of the details could be difficult to capture with crayons, but you can certainly use them if you prefer. If you use markers, slip a scrap piece of paper between the pages in case of bleed-through.

Remember, coloring should be relaxing and that includes relaxing your expectation for perfection. My drawings are quirky and certainly not perfect, but I love making them. My intention is to provide you an opportunity to find a calm and pleasant moment in your day. So enjoy!

Thank you so much!

Ronnie

P.S. If you'd like to share your work on social media, please use the hashtag #ronniescoloringcafe so we can all enjoy your masterpieces!

www.ronniewalter.com

Let's get this day started!

GOOD
Morning!

And share a laugh...or two!

Share a cup of
FRIENDSHIP

Pretty girls, pretty flowers!

A circle of happiness!

Unlock your hopes and dreams.

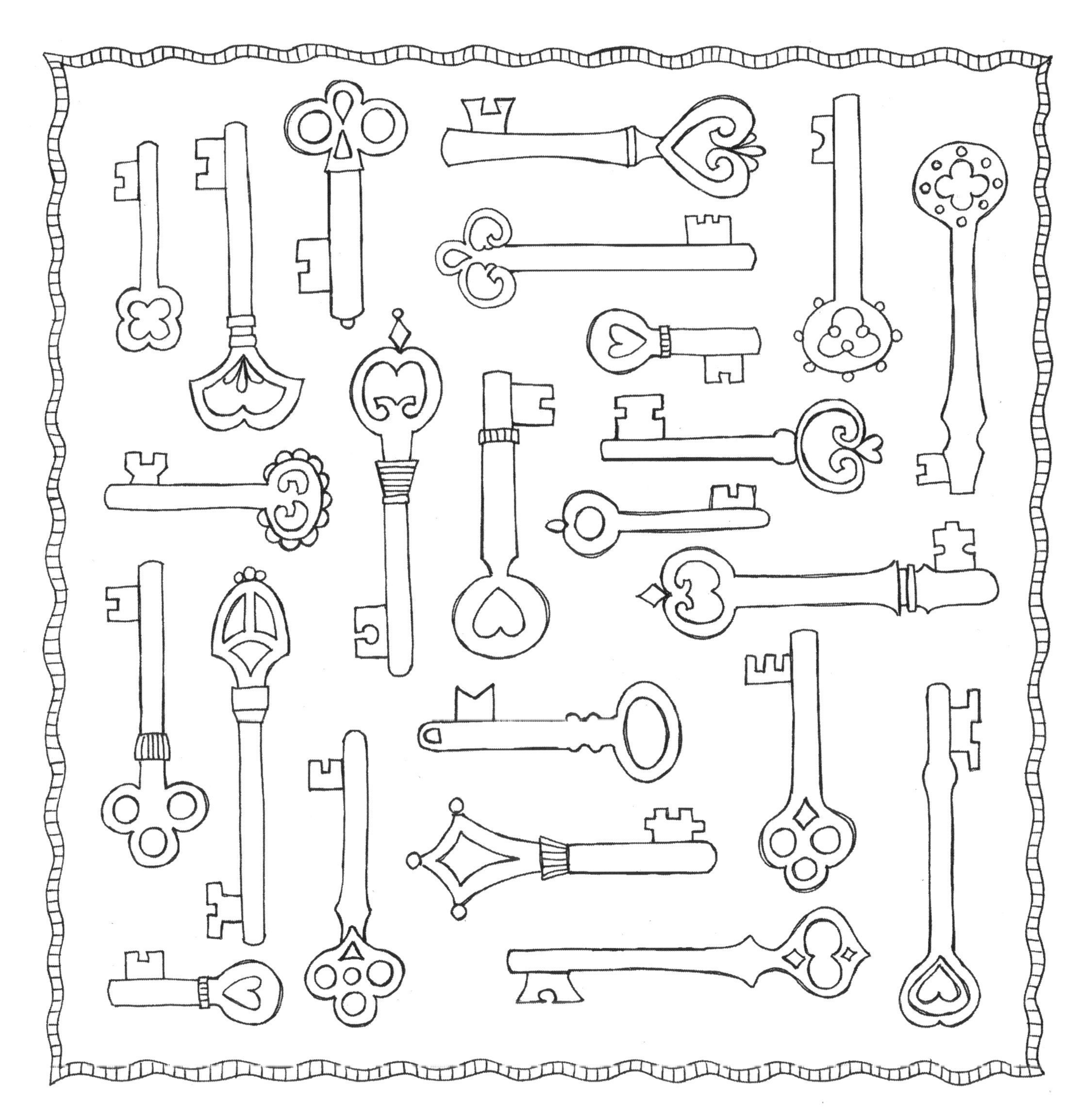

...particularly if they are chocolate!

CUPCAKES
Make me So Very
HAPPY!

You too, right?

I LOVE TO
COLOR

Change your hat, change your mind!

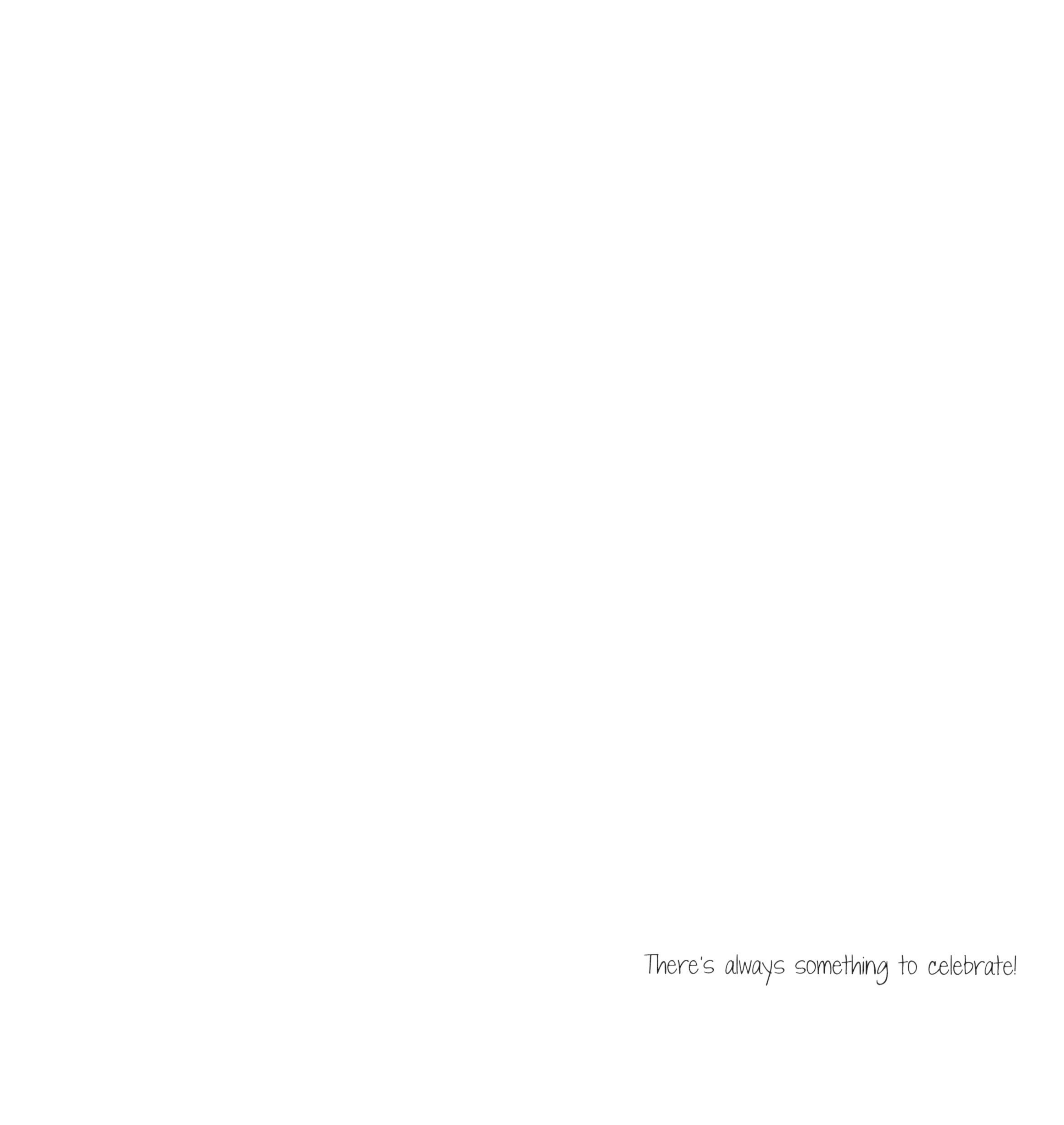
There's always something to celebrate!

That's you!

CUTE as a BUG

Coloring in the round.

What a great way to spend an afternoon.

Cafe

Well, this looks like fun!

A day at the beach is best with good friends!

No matter what!

FOREVER FRIENDS

Cute...and warm!

We believe it, shouldn't you?

BE YOUR
Beautiful
SELF

Relax...enjoy...color!

Where's the party?

Caffiene makes it all possible!

Saving the World
ONE CUP OF
COFFEE
AT A TIME

Pretty, patterned paisley...

Hoooo-ooo is the cute one?

They make the outfit you know!

How Tragic To
Lack The
Ability To
Accessorize

Yes, you!

YOU,
MY DEAR...
ARE A
STAR!

A garden of color.

A pair of boots and you're ready for anything!

And watch it grow...

Plant
the
Seeds
of
Love

It all starts here...

Adding a little fun to life!

Have lots of fun together!

BIRDS of a FEATHER

Going somewhere, my dear?

Have cute purse, will travel.

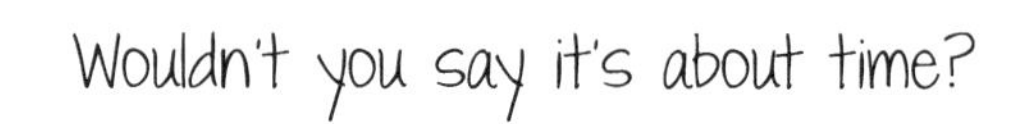
Wouldn't you say it's about time?

Tea Time

...and coffee, of course!

I LOVE
FASHION

Because life can be a roller coaster!

GRAB ON,
HOLD ON TIGHT...
and
HAVE A
BLAST!

Life is a rainbow!

Friends come in all shapes and sizes.

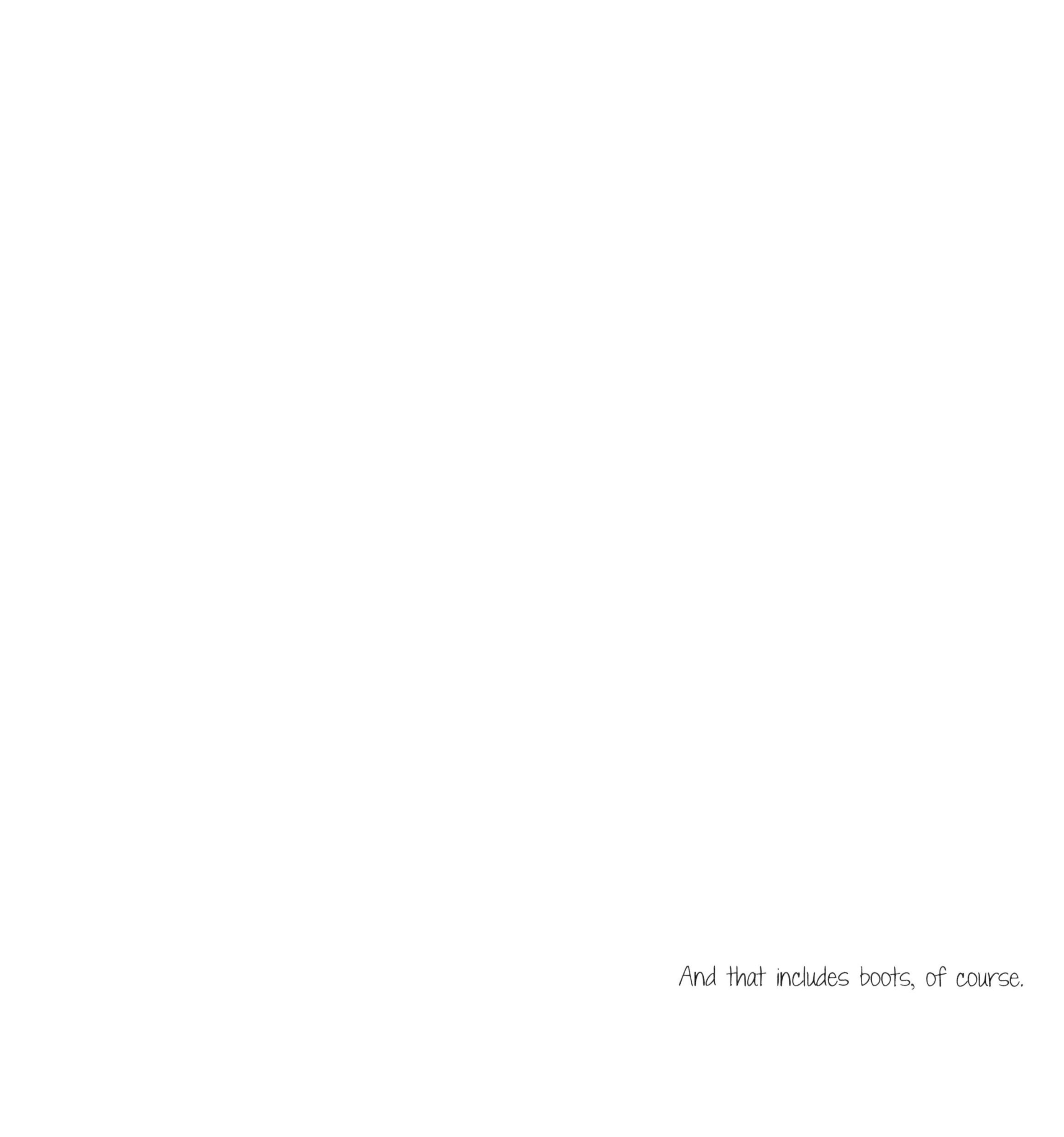

And that includes boots, of course.

I Love SHOES

Three of my favorite things...

DREAM
Imagine
BELIEVE
LOVE

Flowers make me smile.

Just add cute shoes!

Linked by love...

FRIENDS
FOREVER OR APART
always
HEART to HEART

Pick one out and off we go!

It just makes life easier.

Choose
LOVE
Today

Bright blossoms to color...

Your future's so bright...

And find the smallest beauties.

Enjoy
this
Day

Sleep tight!

GOOD
Night!

About The Artist

Ronnie Walter is an illustrator and award winning writer. She licenses her illustrations on all kind of products including stickers, greeting cards, stationery, giftware, fabric and more.

She is the author of License to Draw! How I Built a Fun Career in Art Licensing and You Can Too! and Gruesome Greetings, A Georgie Hardtman Mystery, both available in paperback and Kindle.

Ronnie lives in paradise with her husband Jim and the best shelter dog ever, Larry.

Facebook: Coloring Cafe
Instagram: @ronniewalter
Twitter: @myfriendronnie
www.ronniewalter.com

Made in the USA
Middletown, DE
06 August 2015